16
Merry
Christmas!
(2 The Waldrons)

Other books in this series:
Our Baby's Record Book
Our Family Record Book
Golf Score Book
Household Record Book

Also for Cooks by Exley:
An Illustrated Cook's Notebook
Cooks Quotations
Guest Book

BORDER ILLUSTRATIONS BY JUDITH O'DWYER
Published simultaneously in 1993 by Exley Publications in
Great Britain, and Exley Giftbooks in the USA.
Second printing 1994.

Copyright © Helen Exley 1993.

ISBN 1-85015-447-3

Edited and pictures selected by Helen Exley.
Designed by Pinpoint Design.
Picture research by P. A. Goldberg and J. M. Clift, Image Select,
London.
Typeset by Delta, Watford.
Printed at Oriental Press, UAE.

Exley Publications Ltd, 16 Chalk Hill, Watford,
Herts WD1 4BN, United Kingdom.

Exley Giftbooks, 232 Madison Avenue, Suite 1206,
NY 10016, USA.

My Best

RECIPES

EDITED BY
HELEN EXLEY

EXLEY
NEW YORK • WATFORD, UK

INTRODUCTION

This book is designed for you to make your very own. It's been deliberately made as flexible as possible so you can use it as suits you best.

Its unstructured form is ideal for recording whatever recipes you choose – you won't be bound by headings or limited to a certain number of dishes per course. The layout is as open as possible to cater for all styles of cooks – there's nothing to stop you from recording forty bread recipes and nothing else, if that's your thing!

To make things as helpful as possible the pages are numbered, and there is a blank contents page for you to fill in your collection of recipes. This acts as a handy organizer – no matter how jumbled your choice of tasty meals may be.

Have fun!
HELEN EXLEY

CONTENTS

FOR YOU TO FILL IN YOUR OWN RECIPE TITLES

INGREDIENTS

METHOD

TITLE OF RECIPE:

INGREDIENTS

METHOD

INGREDIENTS

METHOD

INGREDIENTS

METHOD

INGREDIENTS

METHOD

INGREDIENTS

METHOD

INGREDIENTS

METHOD

TITLE OF RECIPE:

INGREDIENTS

METHOD

INGREDIENTS

METHOD

INGREDIENTS

METHOD

INGREDIENTS

METHOD

INGREDIENTS

METHOD

TITLE OF RECIPE:

INGREDIENTS

METHOD

INGREDIENTS

METHOD

INGREDIENTS

METHOD

INGREDIENTS

METHOD

INGREDIENTS

METHOD

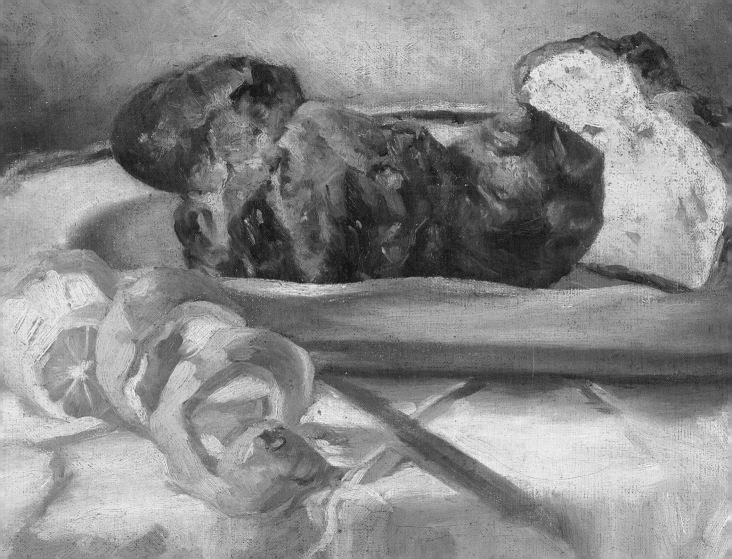

TITLE OF RECIPE:

INGREDIENTS

METHOD

INGREDIENTS

METHOD

INGREDIENTS

METHOD

INGREDIENTS

METHOD

INGREDIENTS

METHOD

INGREDIENTS

METHOD

INGREDIENTS

METHOD

INGREDIENTS

METHOD

INGREDIENTS

METHOD

INGREDIENTS

METHOD

PAGE 47   TITLE OF RECIPE:

Ingredients

Method

INGREDIENTS

METHOD

INGREDIENTS

METHOD

INGREDIENTS

METHOD

INGREDIENTS

METHOD

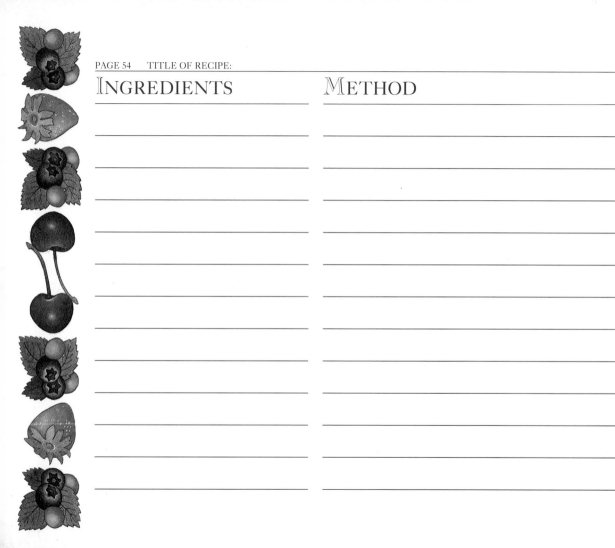

PAGE 54   TITLE OF RECIPE:

INGREDIENTS

METHOD

INGREDIENTS

METHOD

INGREDIENTS

METHOD

INGREDIENTS

METHOD

INGREDIENTS

METHOD

INGREDIENTS

METHOD

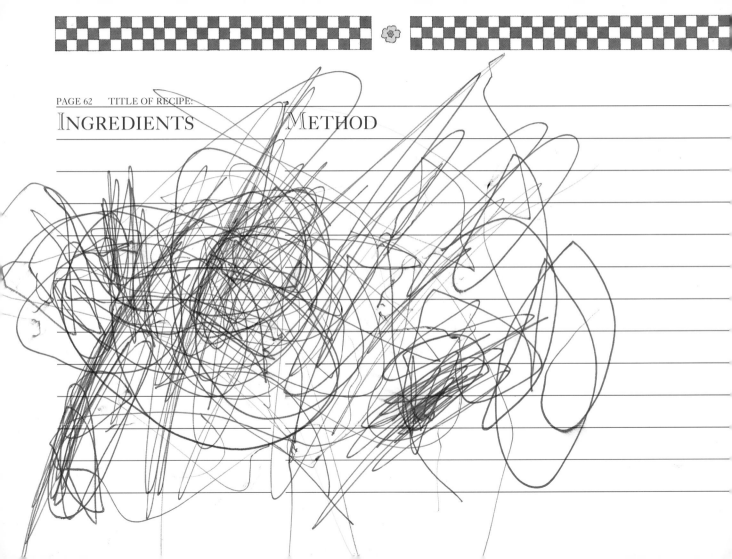

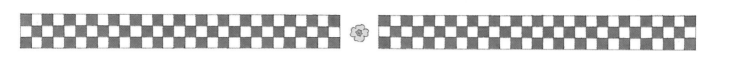

TITLE OF RECIPE:

INGREDIENTS

METHOD

INGREDIENTS

METHOD

INGREDIENTS

METHOD

Ingredients

Method

INGREDIENTS

METHOD

INGREDIENTS

METHOD

INGREDIENTS

METHOD

INGREDIENTS

METHOD

INGREDIENTS

METHOD

INGREDIENTS

METHOD

INGREDIENTS

METHOD

INGREDIENTS

METHOD

INGREDIENTS

METHOD

HERBERT E. HARLEY.

INGREDIENTS

METHOD

INGREDIENTS

METHOD

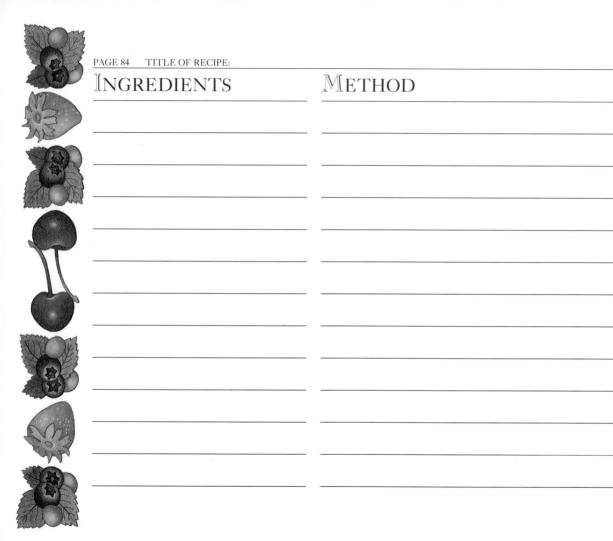

INGREDIENTS

METHOD

INGREDIENTS

METHOD

ACKNOWLEDGEMENTS

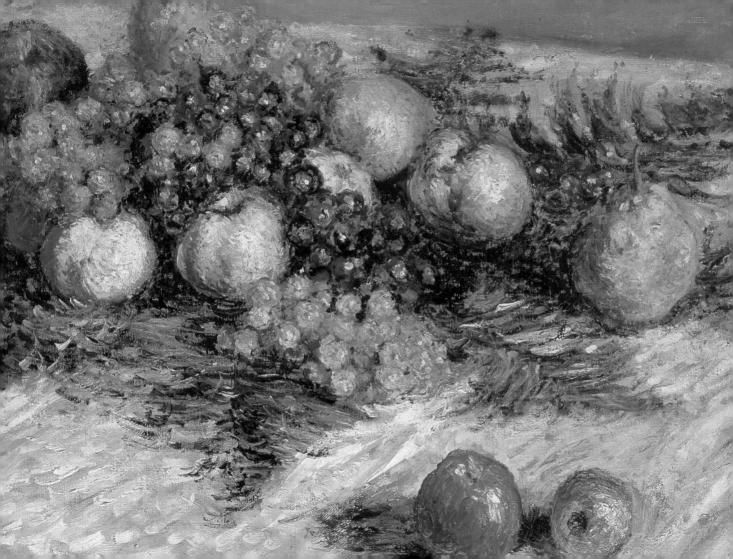